How Flamingos Came to Have Red Legs

A South American Folktale

Contents

Retold by Ned Jensen
Illustrated by Madeline Beasley

Chapter 1
Time for a Party

It had been a very long, cold winter, but now the ice had started to melt from the lakes. The flowers were blooming, the birds were singing once again, and everyone was happy. Spring was coming.

The snakes slithered up from their holes deep in the ground and sunned themselves in the warm sun. Everything was good. In fact, everything was so good that the snakes decided to have a party and invite all the animals that lived near the lake.

They invited the frogs and the toads. They invited the fish and the alligators. And they invited the pretty pink flamingos. The snakes told all the animals to wear their party clothes. They wanted it to be the biggest party of the year.

Chapter 2

The Snakes' Party

6

The fish said they wouldn't come to the party because they had no legs and wouldn't be able to dance. But the snakes wanted the fish to come so they held the party at the edge of the lake. The fish sat up on their tails, and when something pleased them, they splashed the water with their fins.

The alligators came wearing bananas and banana leaves. They wore the yellow bananas around their necks like necklaces, and covered their bodies and tails with the green leaves.

The frogs were happy to come in their smooth, green skins but bathed in sweet-smelling perfumes. The toads stuck fish scales all over their bodies to hide their ugly warts and carried lightning bugs on the end of a string. In the darkness of the night, the lightning bugs glowed like lanterns.

The toads were the first animals on the dance floor. They danced as if they were swimming, moving their legs in and out. The fish splashed about in the water and made fun of the dancing toads, but the frogs thought the toads looked just fine in their green and blue fish scales.

The snakes were the best dressed of all the animals. They slithered in wearing gowns of yellow, red, green, pink, and orange. Each snake's gown was different.

Of all the snakes at the party, the coral snakes were the best dressed, in their gowns of red, black, and white. They looked so beautiful that everybody wanted to dance with them.

The flamingos were the only animals that weren't having fun. They hadn't dressed up for the party. No one wanted to dance with them, and they were bored.

The fish splashed about in the water and made fun of the flamingos' white legs. The flamingos looked on at the coral snakes' gowns and wished they had worn bright clothes.

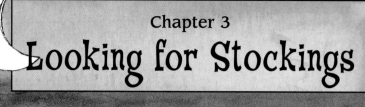

Chapter 3
Looking for Stockings

Then, one of the flamingos had a great idea.

"Why don't we go and get some stockings to cover our white legs," it said. "The coral snakes will want to dance with us if we are wearing bright stockings."

So the flamingos left the party and flew to a small stocking shop in a nearby village.

Once there, the flamingos banged on the door.

"Who's there?" called the stocking shop owner. "What do you want?"

"We are flamingos, and we are here to get bright stockings," the flamingos shouted loudly. "We want to wear them to the snakes' party, then the coral snakes will want to dance with us."

"Are you crazy?" said the stocking shop owner, "I have stockings for people, not for silly birds!"

So the flamingos flew to another stocking shop, and again they banged on the door.

"Open up!" the flamingos shouted.

Again the stocking shop owner asked them what they wanted, and when they told him, he said they were crazy, too. The flamingos flew to more stocking shops, but each time they were told they were crazy. They felt very sad they hadn't found any bright stockings and began to fly back to the party.

Chapter 4
Stockings for Flamingos

An old owl named Tatu had heard about the snakes' party and the flamingos who wanted some bright stockings. Tatu flew to meet the flamingos as they were flying over the lake.

"I hear you're looking for some bright stockings to wear," he said to the flamingos. "I don't think you can get any near here, but Ma Barn Owl has some. Why don't you go and see her?"

17

So the flamingos flew to see Ma Barn Owl.

"We have no party clothes for the snakes' party," they said to her. "Tatu said you'd help us. The coral snakes will dance with us if we are wearing bright stockings."

"I would be most pleased to help you," said Ma Barn Owl. "Please wait here."

Ma Barn Owl flew away. When she came back, she had what looked like bright stockings hanging from her beak.

But they weren't real stockings. They were the skins of coral snakes the owls had caught and eaten.

The flamingos were very excited and didn't take the time to look at the stockings. They just pulled them on over their white legs and thought about dancing with the coral snakes.

With their stockings, the flamingos were ready to fly back to the party. But before they did, Ma Barn Owl told them one thing – be sure not to stop dancing.

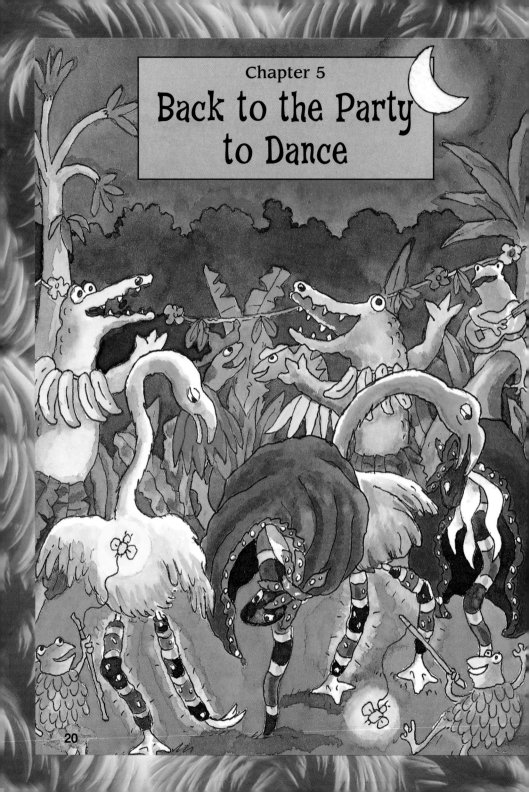

Chapter 5
Back to the Party to Dance

When the flamingos got to the party, the other animals stopped dancing and looked at the flamingos' bright stockings. All the animals wanted to dance with them, even the coral snakes.

The flamingos didn't forget what Ma Barn Owl had told them. They danced, and they danced, and they danced. The more the coral snakes danced with the flamingos, the more the coral snakes wondered if the flamingos were wearing real stockings. But as long as the flamingos danced, the coral snakes couldn't get close to look at their stockings.

As the night went on, the dancing flamingos grew very tired. Finally, one flamingo tripped over an alligator's tail and was too tired to get back up.

The coral snakes took their chance. They grabbed the toads' lanterns and they looked closely at the flamingo's stockings.

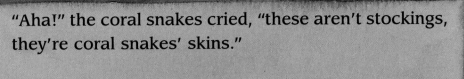

"Aha!" the coral snakes cried, "these aren't stockings, they're coral snakes' skins."

The coral snakes were very angry. They started to bite at the flamingos' legs and rip off their stockings. The snakes didn't stop until they had ripped every snake skin from every flamingo's leg.

The flamingos, with their legs all raw and red, walked into the cool water of the lake to stop the pain and wash away the red.

But they couldn't wash away the red, and even today flamingos still walk in water to try to wash the red from their legs. And that is the story of how flamingos came to have red legs.